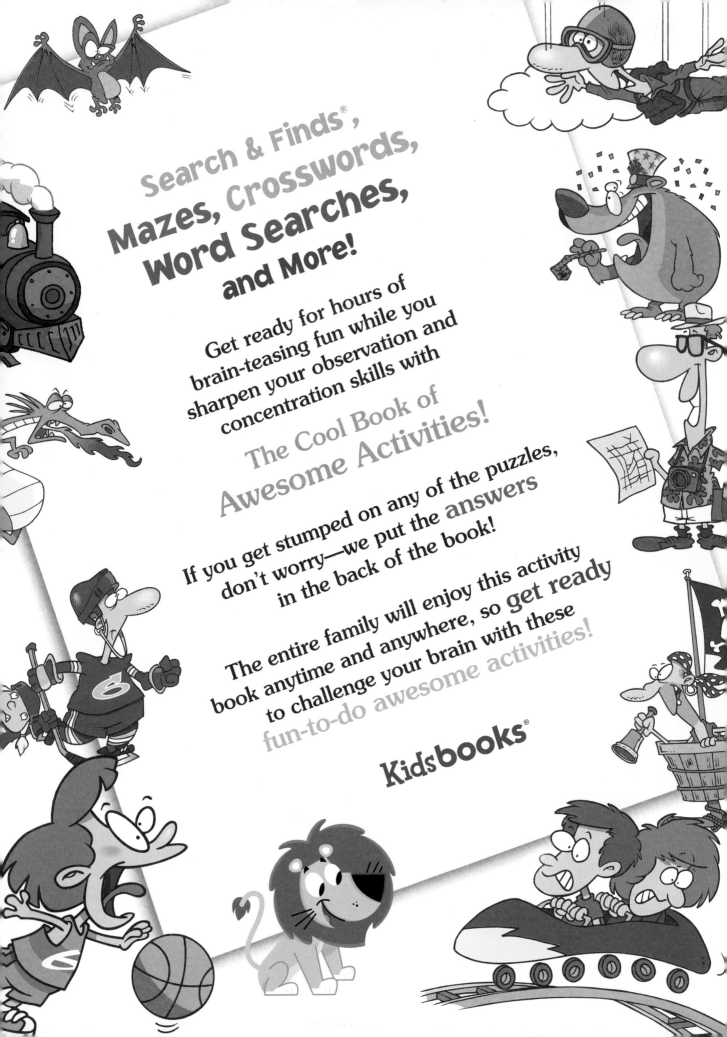

Search & Finds®, Mazes, Crosswords, Word Searches, and More!

Get ready for hours of brain-teasing fun while you sharpen your observation and concentration skills with

The Cool Book of Awesome Activities!

If you get stumped on any of the puzzles, don't worry—we put the answers in the back of the book!

The entire family will enjoy this activity book anytime and anywhere, so get ready to challenge your brain with these fun-to-do awesome activities!

Kidsbooks®

Double Ships

Can you find the two pictures that are exactly alike?

4

Answer on page 27

Situational

Can you make **25** words or more from this word?

SITUATIONAL

Sit

Tin

Ton

Snot

Nut

National

Snout

Answer on page 27

Ferris Wheel

Follow the path from **Start** to **Finish** to
go around the Ferris wheel.

START

FINISH

Answer on page 27

Relationships

Use the pictures below to complete this crossword puzzle.

Going to the City

Find **three sets of two objects** that rhyme with each other.

Answer on page 28

The Pet Shop

Search, find, and circle these **10** things.

WITCH'S HAT ✓
COMPASS ✓
STOPLIGHT ✓

APPLE ✓
DOUGHNUT ✓
JACK-O'-LANTERN ✓
KEYBOARD ✓

MUSHROOM
HOCKEY STICK
TOOL BELT ✓

9

Skating Fun

Find **10** differences between the picture on the top and the one on the bottom.

Answer on page 28

Word Scramble

Unscramble each of these words using the clues.

NEFDIR
(Buddy, pal)

F R I E N D

LITSEHO
(Not friendly)

_ _ _ _ _ _ _

AELNCRE
(Fresher, not dirty)

_ _ _ _ _ _ _

ENDCOS
(Not first)

_ _ _ _ _ _

IPNOTRO
(Part, piece)

_ _ _ _ _ _ _

TKAACT
(Assault)

_ _ _ _ _ _

EWOHRS
(Sprinkle)

S H O W E R

ITRNAUC
(Drape)

_ _ _ _ _ _ _

11

Indoor Sports

Find these indoor sports in the word search.
Look up, down, backward, forward, and diagonally.

VOLLEYBALL   **GYMNASTICS**
DODGEBALL   **TABLE TENNIS**
RACQUETBALL   **POOL**
SWIMMING   **YOGA**
RUNNING
ICE SKATING

V	T	S	C	I	T	S	A	N	M	Y	G	G	D
B	A	R	Z	C	Y	N	P	F	R	D	N	R	O
A	B	W	Q	K	L	F	D	U	M	I	Q	I	D
O	L	V	C	Y	U	Z	N	D	T	D	C	R	G
D	E	P	A	Q	Z	N	N	A	B	G	A	C	E
X	T	X	M	G	I	C	K	E	R	C	L	T	B
G	E	V	N	N	O	S	P	A	Q	O	N	N	A
N	N	I	G	K	E	Y	R	U	O	Z	T	R	L
I	N	M	S	C	P	H	E	P	A	U	H	X	L
M	I	B	I	Q	U	T	R	D	L	Y	X	U	B
M	S	L	L	A	B	Y	E	L	L	O	V	O	K
I	J	L	W	A	W	E	H	U	O	U	S	D	F
W	B	Q	L	M	K	A	J	K	H	T	X	U	Y
S	C	L	X	K	A	E	S	W	H	O	T	J	Z

Answer on page 29

Haunted House

Follow the path from **Start** to **Finish** to go from
the bottom of the haunted house to the top.

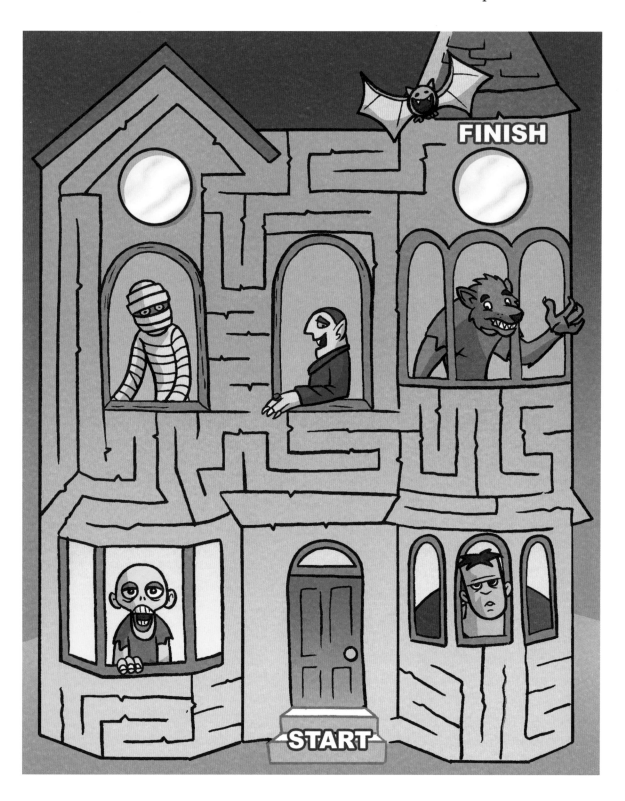

Answer on page 29

Decode-a-Riddle

Write the letter that comes **AFTER** each letter shown below to decode and solve this riddle.

H E   X N T   O T S   Z

A K T D   G Z S   H M S N

S G D   Q D C   R D Z

V G Z S   C N D R   H S

A D B N L D ?

V D S

Double Squirrels

Can you find the two pictures that are exactly alike?

Answer on page 29

Flabbergasted

Can you make **15** words or more, of
5 or more letters, from the following word?

FLABBERGASTED

Robot Maze

Follow the path from **Start** to **Finish** to
get the robots to the finish line.

Answer on page 30

Into the Forest

Find **two sets of two objects** that rhyme
with each other.

Answer on page 30

Outer Space

Search, find, and circle these **10** things.

CRAYONS IN BOX   LADYBUG   DICE
BEAR   PIG   PRAIRIE DOG
PALM TREE   WITCH   SNAKE
GIRL WITH PIGTAILS

Answer on page 30

Back to School

Find **10** differences between the picture on the top and the one on the bottom.

Answer on page 31

Word Scramble

Unscramble each of these words using the clues.

DINECMIE
(Makes you better)

_ _ _ _ _ _ _ _

KMKESILHA
(Ice-cream drink)

_ _ _ _ _ _ _ _ _

RHETCEA
(Learning professional)

_ _ _ _ _ _ _

REPENPASW
(Printed current events)

_ _ _ _ _ _ _ _ _

SMTASTRE
(Where one sleeps)

_ _ _ _ _ _ _ _

DYWBRAOA
(Where plays are performed)

_ _ _ _ _ _ _ _

NSTREMO
(Scary creature)

_ _ _ _ _ _ _

MEILACMORC
(Sells ads)

_ _ _ _ _ _ _ _ _ _

21

Answer on page 31

Odd Stuff

Replace every letter in the puzzle with the one that comes **before** it in the alphabet to find out why the man is so upset.

A B C D E F G H I J K L M
N O P Q R S T U V W X Y Z

U I F S F

J T

B

G M Z

J O

I J T

T P V Q

___ ___ ___ ___ ___   ___ ___   ___

___ ___ ___   ___ ___   ___ ___ ___   ___ ___ ___ ___!

It's All Relative

Use the clues below to complete this crossword puzzle.

ACROSS
3 Second ____, once removed
6 Child of one's child
9 Your parent's sister
10 Female sibling
11 Female parent
12 Your mother's mother

DOWN
1 Male sibling
2 Male child
4 Your father's father
5 Your parent's brother
7 Female child
8 Male parent

23

Decode-a-Message

Use the code key below to find something
that has to do with another world.

A=6	F=1	M=2	P=5	T=10
C=9	I=4	N=14	R=7	U=13
E=12	L=8	O=11	S=3	

6 8 4 12 14 3   1 7 11 2

11 13 10 12 7   3 5 6 9 12

Answer on page 32

Which is Witch?

Can you find the two pictures that are exactly alike?

Answer on page 32

Encyclopedia

Can you make **15** words or more, of
5 or more letters, from the following word?

ENCYCLOPEDIA

Answer on page 32

Answers

Page 4
Double Ships

Page 5
Situational

SITUATIONAL

Here are just a few:

alas	list	sail	sun
also	lit	salt	tail
alto	loan	sat	tan
ant	lost	sit	tilt
aunt	lots	slit	tin
auto	nail	slot	tint
into	not	soil	toil
its	nut	son	ton
last	oat	soul	tot
lint	oil	stun	tuna
lion	out	suit	unit

Page 6
Ferris Wheel

Page 7
Relationships

27

Answers

Page 8
Going to the City

Page 9
The Pet Shop

Page 10
Skating Fun

Page 11
Word Scramble

NEFDIR
(Buddy, pal)
F R I E N D

AELNCRE
(Fresher, not dirty)
C L E A N E R

IPNOTRO
(Part, piece)
P O R T I O N

EWOHRS
(Sprinkle)
S H O W E R

LITSEHO
(Not friendly)
H O S T I L E

ENDCOS
(Not first)
S E C O N D

TKAACT
(Assault)
A T T A C K

ITRNAUC
(Drape)
C U R T A I N

Answers

Page 12
Indoor Sports

VOLLEYBALL   GYMNASTICS
DODGEBALL   TABLE TENNIS
RACQUETBALL   POOL
SWIMMING   YOGA
RUNNING
ICE SKATING

```
V T S C I T S A N M Y G G D
B A R Z C Y N P F R D N R O
A B W Q K L F D U M I Q I D
O L V C Y U Z N D T D C R G
D E P A Q Z N N A B G A C E
X T X M G I C K E R C L T B
G E N N O S P A Q O N N A
N N I G K E Y R U O Z T R L
I M S C P H E P A U H X L
M S B I Q U T R D L Y X U B
M L L A B Y E L L O V O K
I J L W A W E H U O U S D F
W B Q L M K A J K H T X U Y
S C L X K A E S W H O T J Z
```

Page 13
Haunted House

Page 14
Decode-a-Riddle

I F   Y O U   P U T   A
H E   X N T   O T S   Z

B L U E   H A T   I N T O
A K T D   G Z S   H M S N

T H E   R E D   S E A
S G D   Q D C   R D Z

W H A T   D O E S   I T
V G Z S   C N D R   H S

B E C O M E?
A D B N L D

W E T
V D S

Page 15
Double Squirrels

29

Answers

Page 16

Flabbergasted

FLABBERGASTED

Here are just a few:

after	blast	federal	related
agreed	bread	flags	safer
alert	dabble	fleas	salad
algebra	darts	garbled	salted
altered	deals	gates	sealed
atlas	dearest	glade	sleet
badge	debater	grabbed	stable
badger	defeat	grated	staged
bagel	desert	greased	stare
barge	eager	great	steed
beagle	eagle	large	table
bearable	eater	later	teased
beard	erase	least	trade
beast	fable	rafts	trees
beatable	false	readable	
beret	faster	rebate	
blade	feast	rebels	

Page 17

Robot Maze

Page 18

Into the Forest

Page 19

Outer Space

COOL BOOK of awesome activities

Kidsbooks®